KT-412-351

This book belongs to

....

Copyright © 2021

make believe ideas ltd

The Wilderness, Berkhamsted, Hertfordshire, HP4 2AZ, UK.
6th Floor, South Bank House, Barrow Street, Dublin 4, D04 TR29, Ireland.

www.makebelieveideas.co.uk

Photographs courtesy of Shutterstock unless noted as follows:
Make Believe Ideas: 17tl (frog).

What a **SIGHT** **I SAW** last night

by Mary Atkinson

make believe ideas

Get the most from this reader

Before reading:

- Look at the pictures and discuss them together. Ask questions such as, "What is the cat wearing?"

- Relate the topic to your child's world. For example, say: "Can you describe a dream you've had?"

- Familiarise your child with book vocabulary by using terms such as *word*, *letter*, *title*, *author* and *text*.

During reading:

- Prompt your child to sound out unknown words. Draw attention to neglected middle or end sounds.

- Encourage your child to use the pictures as clues to unknown words.

- Occasionally, ask what might happen next, and then check together as you read on.

● Monitor your child's understanding. Repeated readings can improve fluency and comprehension.

● Keep reading sessions short and enjoyable. Stop if your child becomes tired or frustrated.

• •

After reading:

● Discuss the book. Encourage your child to form opinions with questions such as, "What did you like best about this book?"

● Help your child work through the fun activities at the back of the book. Then ask him or her to reread the story. Praise any improvement.

Let me tell you
what I saw last night.

First, I saw a cat in a bright pink hat.

9

Then, I saw a goat in a yellow boat.

Next, I saw a fox
in some spotty socks.

Then, I saw a frog on our old dog.

Last of all, I saw
a foal score a goal.

21

Discussion Questions

1. What was the frog sitting on?

2. What animal name rhymed with hat?

3. Do you think the girl liked the dream? Why?

∾ Sight Words ∾

Learning sight words helps you read fluently. Practise these sight words from the book. Use them in sentences of your own.

all

what

the

saw

old

our

last

then

⚕ Rhyming Words ⚕

Can you find the rhyming pairs?
Say them aloud.

hat

socks

boat

cat

fox

goat

Writing Practice

Read the words, and then trace them with your finger.

tell

boat

socks

last

next

old

⸎ Silly Sentences ⸎

Have fun filling in the gap in each sentence. Use the ideas below or make up your own.

I saw a .... in purple gloves.

I dreamt I was a ....